100 GRADED CLARINET SOLOS

Published by
Wise Publications
14-15 Berners Street, London W1T 3LJ, UK.

Exclusive Distributors:
Music Sales Limited
Distribution Centre, Newmarket Road,
Bury St Edmunds, Suffolk IP33 3YB, UK.
Music Sales Pty Limited
120 Rothschild Avenue, Rosebery, NSW 2018, Australia.

Order No. AM987041
·   ISBN 13: 978-1-84609-741-6
ISBN 10: 1-84609-741-X

Edited by David Harrison.
Music processed by Paul Ewers Music Design.
Cover design by Michael Bell Design.
Printed in the EU.

Your Guarantee of Quality
As publishers, we strive to produce every book to
the highest commercial standards.
This book has been carefully designed to minimise awkward
page turns and to make playing from it a real pleasure.
Particular care has been given to specifying acid-free, neutral-sized
paper made from pulps which have not been elemental chlorine bleached.
This pulp is from farmed sustainable forests and
was produced with special regard for the environment.
Throughout, the printing and binding have been planned to ensure
a sturdy, attractive publication which should give years of enjoyment.
If your copy fails to meet our high standards,
please inform us and we will gladly replace it.

www.musicsales.com

100 GRADED CLARINET SOLOS

WISE PUBLICATIONS
part of The Music Sales Group

London / New York / Paris / Sydney / Copenhagen / Berlin / Madrid / Tokyo

GRADING NOTES

The pieces in this book have been carefully graded according to
various criteria such as rhythmic complexity, phrasing, tempo, key, range, etc.
Look for the number of stars for each piece to give you
an idea of the approximate playing level.
All musicians have particular strengths and weaknesses,
so the grading offered here should be taken as a suggestion only.

Generally, pieces with one star have simple rhythms,
straight forward phrasings and few difficult intervals;
essentially diatonic and in easier keys.

Pieces with two stars will have more challenging passages,
perhaps containing more rhythmic complexity,
more advanced key signatures and possibly long-held notes
requiring an increased strength of embouchure.

Three-star pieces may include chromaticism,
challenging articulation and more advanced fingerings.
Read through rhythms and keys before playing, and check for
time-signature changes and correct phrasing.

The Air That I Breathe

Words & Music by Albert Hammond & Mike Hazelwood

All I Have To Do Is Dream

Words & Music by Boudleaux Bryant

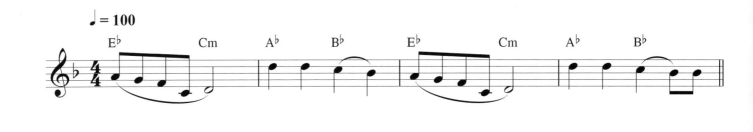

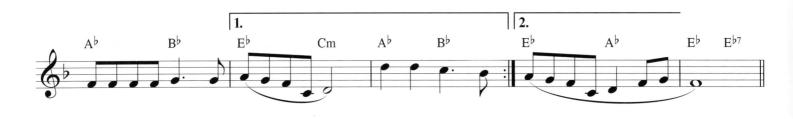

All The Young Dudes

Words & Music by David Bowie

Always On My Mind

Words & Music by Mark James, Wayne Thompson & Johnny Christopher

Angels

Words & Music by Robbie Williams & Guy Chambers

Angie

Words & Music by Mick Jagger & Keith Richards

...Baby One More Time

Words & Music by Max Martin

Bridge Over Troubled Water

Words & Music by Paul Simon

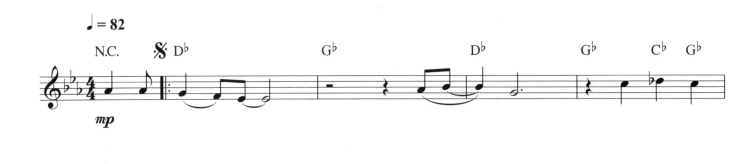

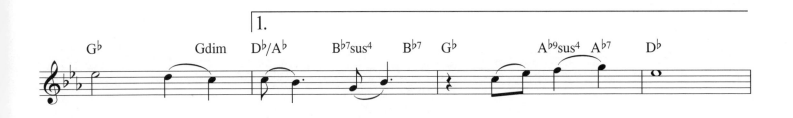

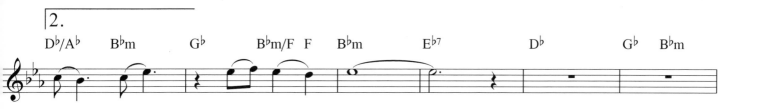

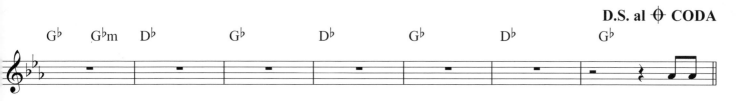

D.S. al ⊕ CODA

⊕ **CODA**

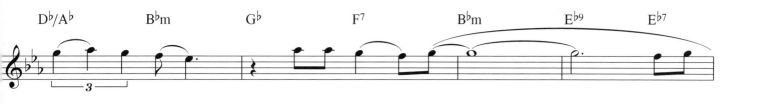

Both Sides Now

Words & Music by Joni Mitchell

The Can Can

Music by Jacques Offenbach

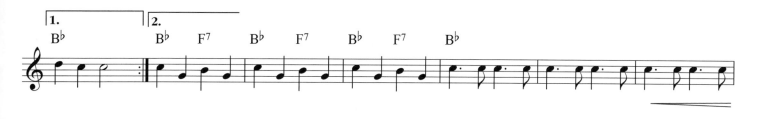

Can't Get You Out Of My Head

Words & Music by Cathy Dennis & Rob Davis

Can't Help Falling In Love

Words & Music by George David Weiss, Hugo Peretti & Luigi Creatore

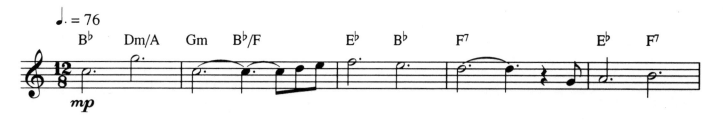

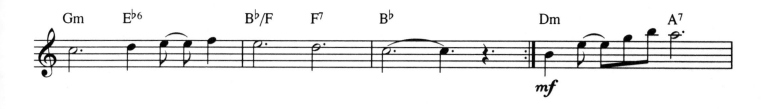

Creep

Words & Music by Thom Yorke, Jonny Greenwood, Colin Greenwood, Ed O'Brien,
Phil Selway, Albert Hammond & Mike Hazlewood

Dancing Queen

Words & Music by Benny Andersson, Stig Anderson & Björn Ulvaeus

Corcovado
(Quiet Nights Of Quiet Stars)

Words & Music by Antonio Carlos Jobim

Don't Cry For Me Argentina

Music by Andrew Lloyd Webber
Lyrics by Tim Rice

Slow Tango

Downtown

Words & Music by Tony Hatch

Repeat to fade

The Closest Thing To Crazy

Words & Music by Mike Batt

Don't Know Why

Words & Music by Jesse Harris

(Everything I Do) I Do It For You

Words by Bryan Adams & Robert John Lange
Music by Michael Kamen

Medium slow

a tempo

rall.

EastEnders

Music by Leslie Osborne & Simon May

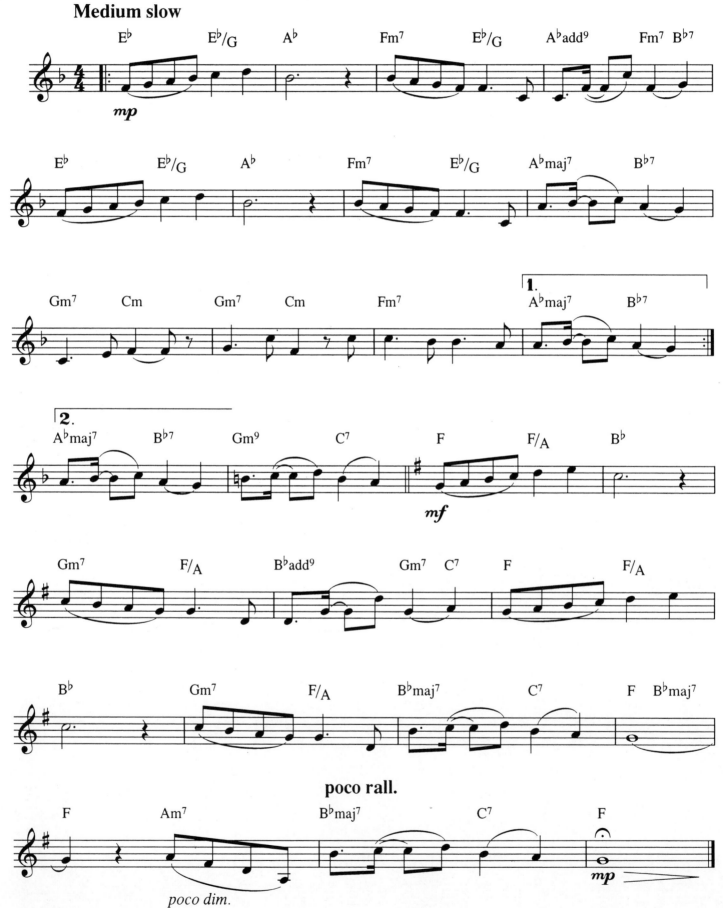

Father And Son

Words & Music by Cat Stevens

The First Cut Is The Deepest

Words & Music by Cat Stevens

Fields Of Gold

Words & Music by Sting

Georgia On My Mind

Words by Stuart Gorrell
Music by Hoagy Carmichael

The Girl From Ipanema
(Garota de Ipanema)

Words by Vinicius De Moraes
Music by Antonio Carlos Jobim

God Only Knows

Words & Music by Brian Wilson & Tony Asher

Good Vibrations

Words & Music by Brian Wilson & Mike Love

Goodbye To Love

Words by John Bettis
Music by Richard Carpenter

Medium slow

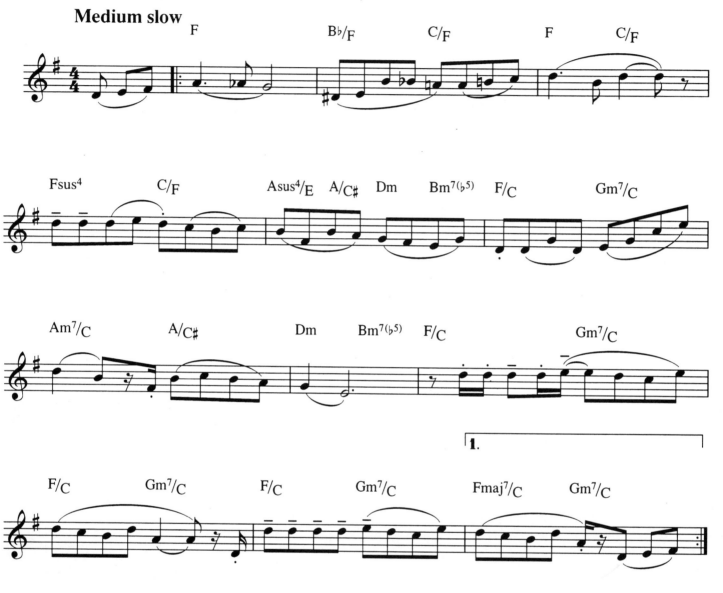

Hallelujah

Words & Music by Leonard Cohen

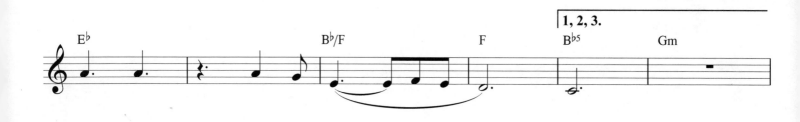

Goldfinger

Words by Leslie Bricusse & Anthony Newley
Music by John Barry

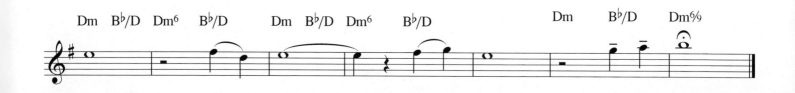

Have A Nice Day

Words & Music by Kelly Jones

Have I Told You Lately

Words & Music by Van Morrison

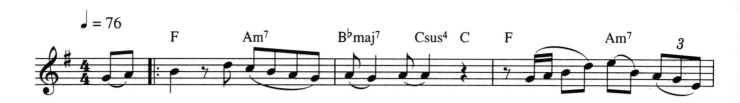

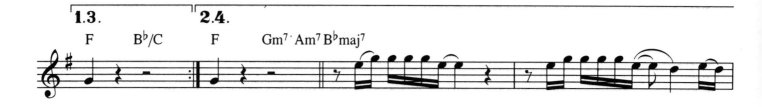

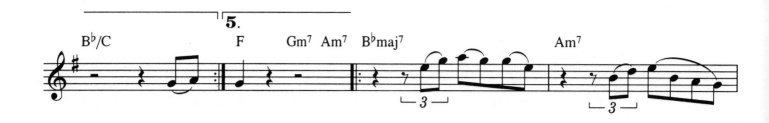

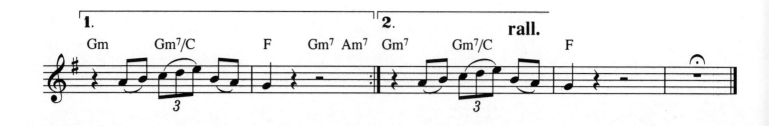

How Deep Is Your Love

Words & Music by Barry Gibb, Maurice Gibb & Robin Gibb

I Believe I Can Fly

Words & Music by R. Kelly

I Left My Heart In San Francisco

Words by Douglas Cross
Music by George Cory

I Will Always Love You

Words & Music by Dolly Parton

It's Not Unusual

Words & Music by Gordon Mills & Les Reed

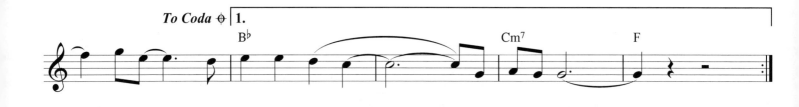

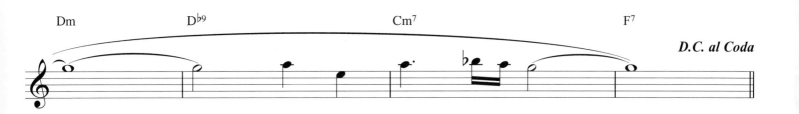

D.C. al Coda

Coda

Fade to end

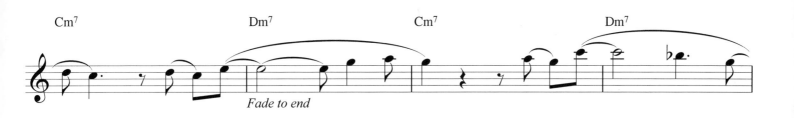

Killing Me Softly With His Song

Words by Norman Gimbel
Music by Charles Fox

Jerusalem

Composed by Hubert Parry

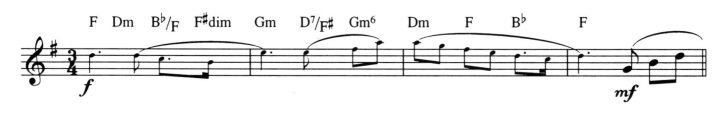

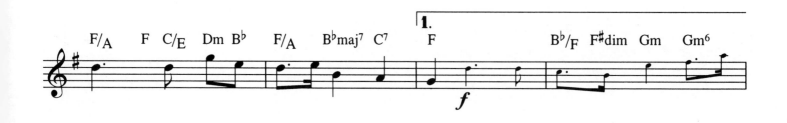

The Lady In Red

Words & Music by Chris de Burgh

Largo
(*from* Symphony No.9 In E Minor)

Composed by Antonín Dvorák

Let It Be

Words & Music by John Lennon & Paul McCartney

Slow and solemn

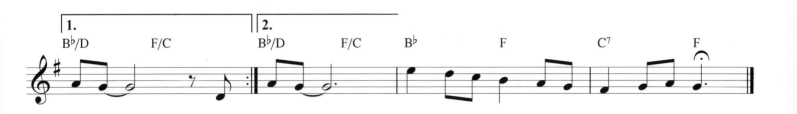

Leave Right Now

Words & Music by Francis White

Let Me Entertain You

Words & Music by Robbie Williams & Guy Chambers

Londonderry Air

Traditional

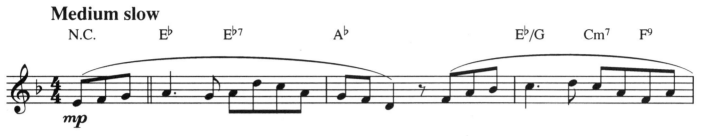

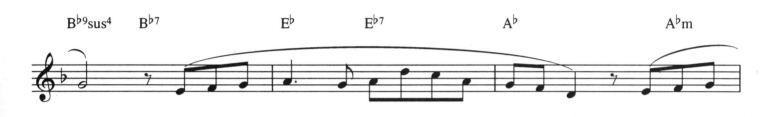

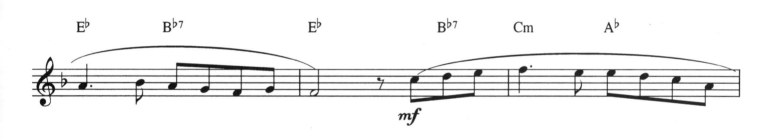

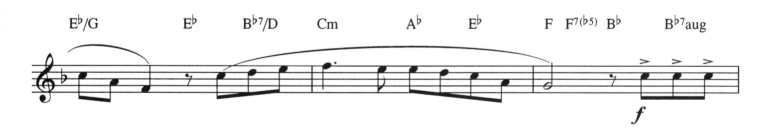

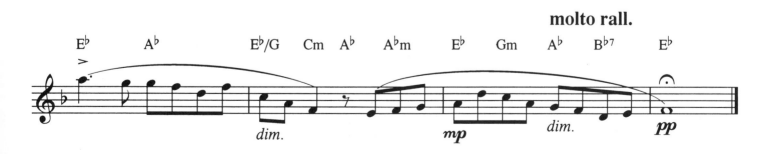

Livin' La Vida Loca

Words & Music By Desmond Child & Robi Rosa

The Long And Winding Road

Words & Music by John Lennon & Paul McCartney

Love And Affection

Words & Music by Joan Armatrading

Love Is All Around

Words & Music by Reg Presley

Mamma Mia

Words & Music by Benny Andersson, Stig Anderson & Björn Ulvaeus

Moon River

Words by Johnny Mercer
Music by Henry Mancini

Waltz tempo

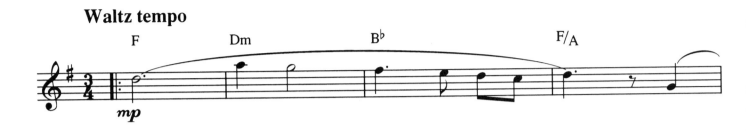

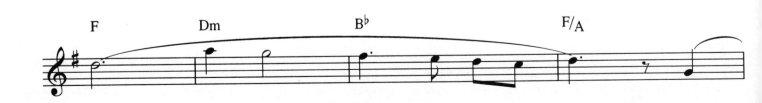

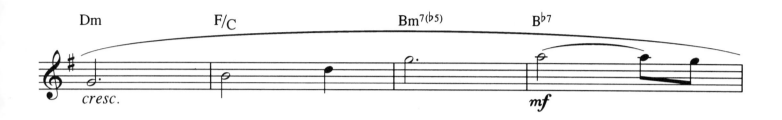

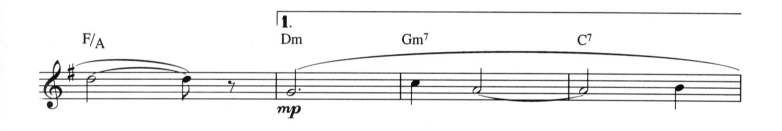

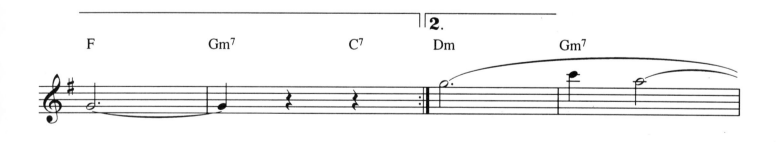

rit.   **a tempo**   **rall.**

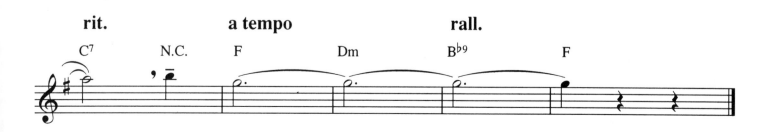

More Than Words

Words & Music by Nuno Bettencourt & Gary Cherone

Message In A Bottle

Words & Music by Sting

Mrs. Robinson

Words & Music by Paul Simon

O Sole Mio

Music by Eduardo Di Capua

Medium tempo

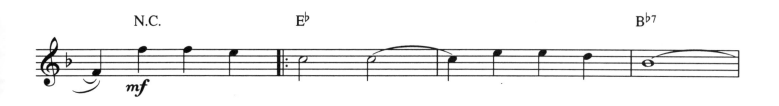

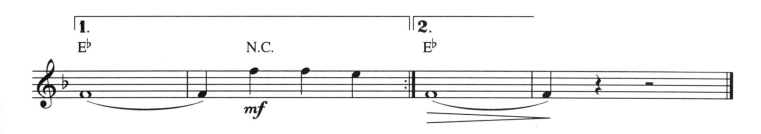

May You Never

Words & Music by John Martyn

Mull Of Kintyre

Words & Music by Paul McCartney & Denny Laine

Nessun Dorma
(*from* Turandot)

Composed by Giacomo Puccini

Perfect

Words & Music by Mark E. Nevin

Put Your Records On

Words & Music by John Beck, Steven Chrisanthou & Corinne Bailey Rae

Raindrops Keep Falling On My Head

Words by Hal David
Music by Burt Bacharach

Medium tempo

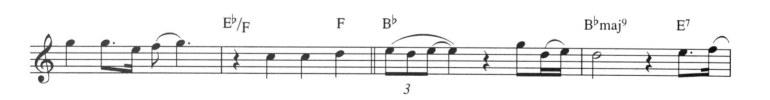

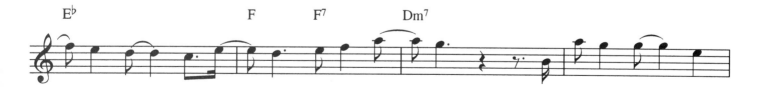

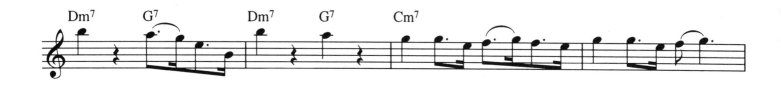

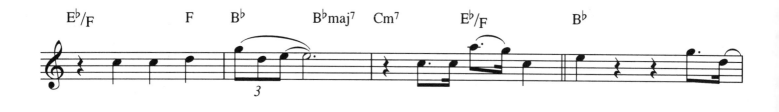

molto rit.

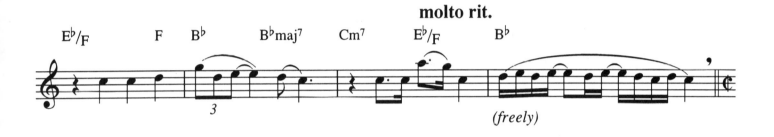

(freely)

Medium fast

Romeo And Juliet

Words & Music by Mark Knopfler

Runaway

Words & Music by Andrea Corr, Caroline Corr, Sharon Corr & Jim Corr

Sail Away

Words & Music by David Gray

Search For The Hero

Words & Music by Mike Pickering & Paul Heard

She's Not There

Words & Music by Rod Argent

She's The One

Words & Music by Karl Wallinger

Something In The Air

Words & Music by John Keen

(Sittin' On) The Dock Of The Bay

Words & Music by Steve Cropper & Otis Redding

Somethin' Stupid

Words & Music by C. Carson Parks

Speak Softly Love
(Love Theme *from* The Godfather)

Words by Larry Kusik
Music by Nino Rota

Stand By Me

Words & Music by Ben E. King, Jerry Leiber & Mike Stoller

Stop

Words & Music by Victoria Aadams, Emma Bunton, Melanie Brown,
Melanie Chisholm, Geri Halliwell, Andy Watkins & Paul Wilson

Strangers In The Night

Words by Charles Singleton & Eddie Snyder
Music by Bert Kaempfert

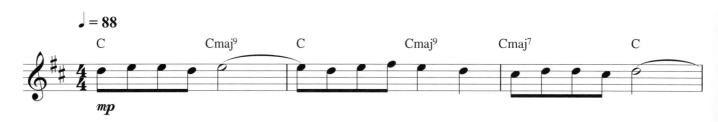

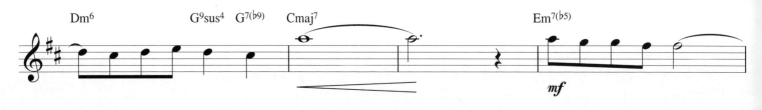

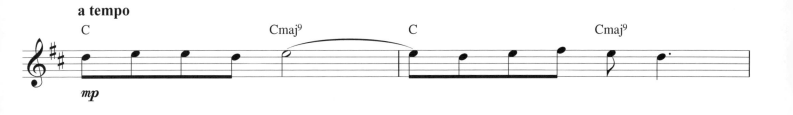

Streets Of London

Words & Music by Ralph McTell

Take Me With U

Words & Music by Prince

Telstar

Music by Joe Meek

Medium tempo

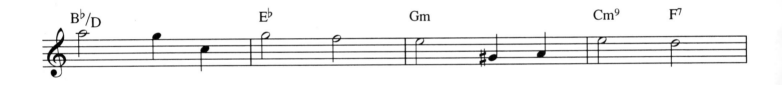

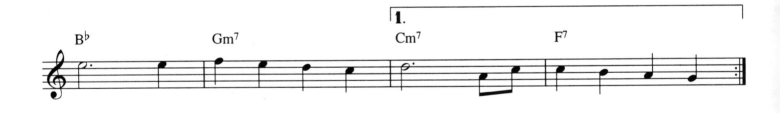

(They Long To Be) Close To You

Words by Hal David
Music by Burt Bacharach

True

Words & Music by Gary Kemp

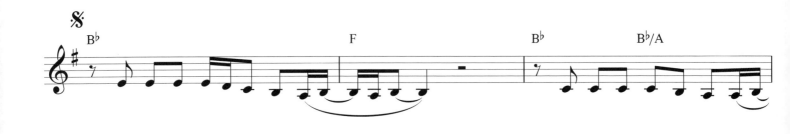

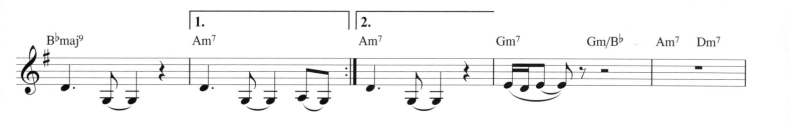

Tears In Heaven

Words & Music by Eric Clapton & Will Jennings

Unchained Melody

Words by Hy Zaret
Music by Alex North

Medium slow

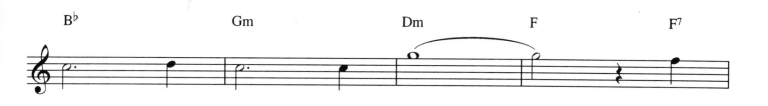

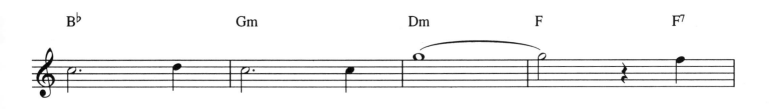

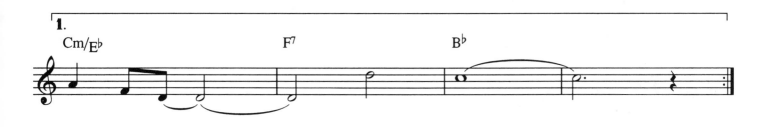

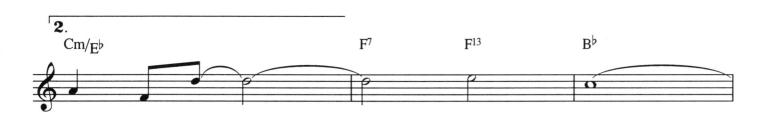

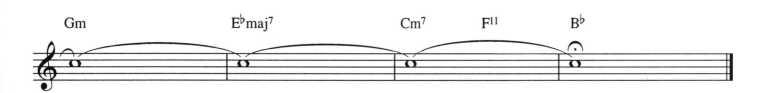

119

Waterloo

Words & Music by Benny Andersson, Stig Anderson & Björn Ulvaeus

When I Need You

Words & Music by Albert Hammond & Carole Bayer Sager

Wedding March
(*from* A Midsummer Night's Dream)

Composed by Felix Mendelssohn

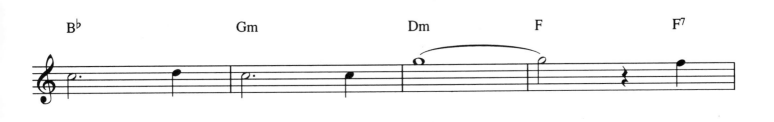

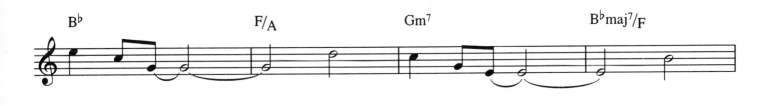

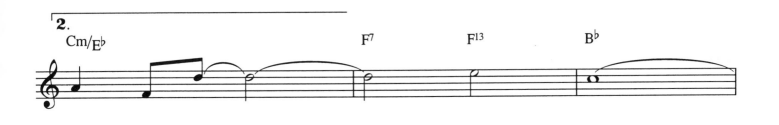

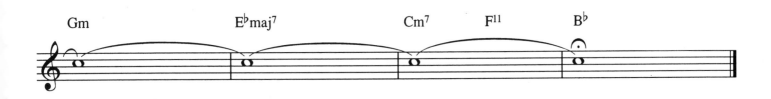

Where Do I Begin
(*Theme from* Love Story)

Words by Carl Sigman
Music by Francis Lai

Medium slow

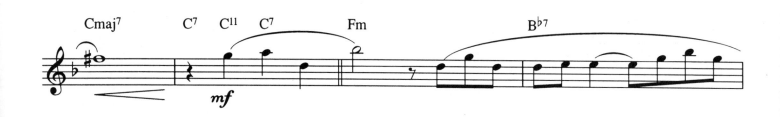

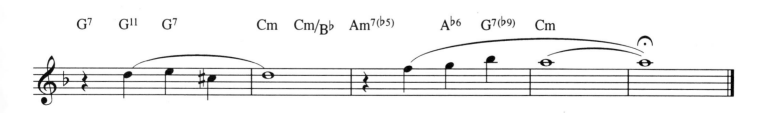

A Whiter Shade Of Pale

Words by Keith Reid
Music by Gary Brooker

Who Do You Think You Are Kidding, Mr. Hitler?
(*Theme from* Dad's Army)

Words & Music by Jimmy Perry & Derek Taverner

Why

Words & Music by Annie Lennox

Winter Wonderland

Words by Richard Smith
Music by Felix Bernard

Why Does It Always Rain On Me?

Words & Music by Fran Healy

131

Wonderful Tonight

Words & Music by Eric Clapton

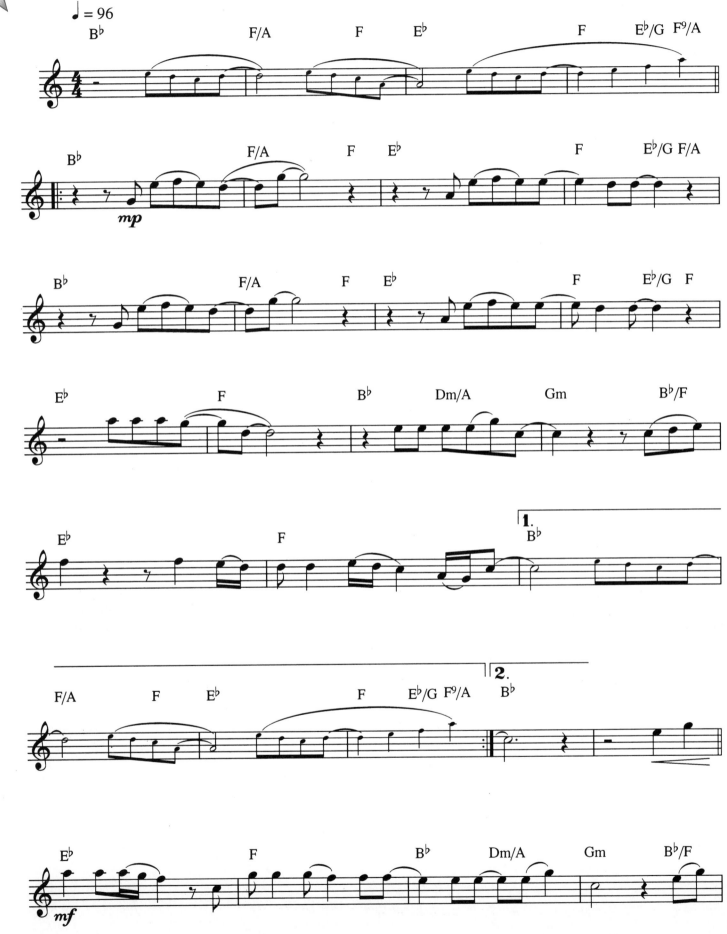

Wonderwall

Words & Music by Noel Gallagher

Woman

Words & Music by John Lennon

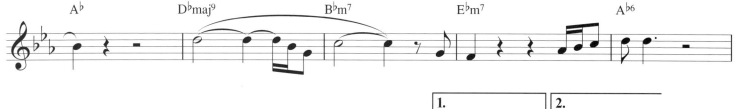

Yellow

Words & Music by Guy Berryman, Jon Buckland, Will Champion & Chris Martin

You're Beautiful

Words & Music by Sacha Skarbek, James Blunt & Amanda Ghost

D.S. al Coda

⊕ *Coda*

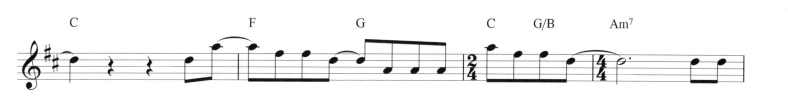

Yesterday

Words & Music by John Lennon & Paul McCartney

Your Song

Words & Music by Elton John & Bernie Taupin

You're So Vain

Words & Music by Carly Simon

Optional: play octave down

Ziggy Stardust

Words & Music by David Bowie

2 3 4 5 6 7 8 9
11/08 (167833)

Bringing you the words and the music

All the latest music in print... rock & pop plus jazz, blues, country, classical and the best in West End show scores.

- Books to match your favourite CDs.

- Book-and-CD titles with high quality backing tracks for you to play along to. Now you can play guitar or piano with your favourite artist... or simply sing along!

- Audition songbooks with CD backing tracks for both male and female singers for all those with stars in their eyes.

- Can't read music? No problem, you can still play all the hits with our wide range of chord songbooks.

- Check out our range of instrumental tutorial titles, taking you from novice to expert in no time at all!

- Musical show scores include *The Phantom Of The Opera*, *Les Misérables*, *Mamma Mia* and many more hit productions.

- DVD master classes featuring the techniques of top artists.

Visit your local music shop or, in case of difficulty, contact the Marketing Department, Music Sales Limited, Newmarket Road, Bury St Edmunds, Suffolk, IP33 3YB, UK
marketing@musicsales.co.uk